School Days, School Ways

Compiled by
Pat Edwards and
Wendy Body

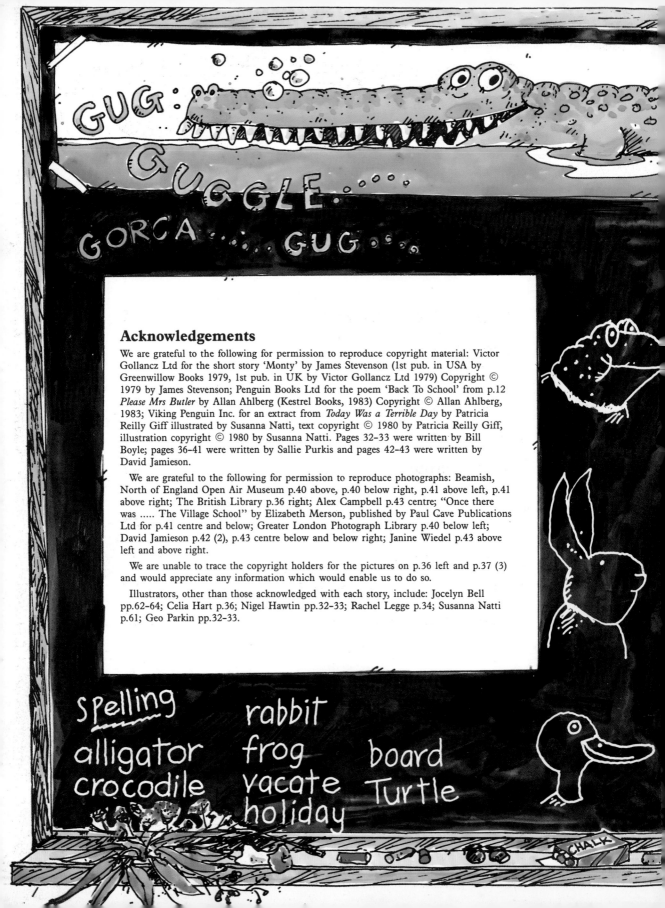

Acknowledgements

We are grateful to the following for permission to reproduce copyright material: Victor Gollancz Ltd for the short story 'Monty' by James Stevenson (1st pub. in USA by Greenwillow Books 1979, 1st pub. in UK by Victor Gollancz Ltd 1979) Copyright © 1979 by James Stevenson; Penguin Books Ltd for the poem 'Back To School' from p.12 *Please Mrs Butler* by Allan Ahlberg (Kestrel Books, 1983) Copyright © Allan Ahlberg, 1983; Viking Penguin Inc. for an extract from *Today Was a Terrible Day* by Patricia Reilly Giff illustrated by Susanna Natti, text copyright © 1980 by Patricia Reilly Giff, illustration copyright © 1980 by Susanna Natti. Pages 32-33 were written by Bill Boyle; pages 36-41 were written by Sallie Purkis and pages 42-43 were written by David Jamieson.

We are grateful to the following for permission to reproduce photographs: Beamish, North of England Open Air Museum p.40 above, p.40 below right, p.41 above left, p.41 above right; The British Library p.36 right; Alex Campbell p.43 centre; "Once there was ..... The Village School" by Elizabeth Merson, published by Paul Cave Publications Ltd for p.41 centre and below; Greater London Photograph Library p.40 below left; David Jamieson p.42 (2), p.43 centre below and below right; Janine Wiedel p.43 above left and above right.

We are unable to trace the copyright holders for the pictures on p.36 left and p.37 (3) and would appreciate any information which would enable us to do so.

Illustrators, other than those acknowledged with each story, include: Jocelyn Bell pp.62-64; Celia Hart p.36; Nigel Hawtin pp.32-33; Rachel Legge p.34; Susanna Natti p.61; Geo Parkin pp.32-33.

CONTENTS

Rules for our class

Always get your home work signed.

Never eat in class.

Never splash water on people.

If you are a monitor, don't forget to water the plants.

Always be kind to each other.

MONTY

EVERY MORNING, ARTHUR AND
DORIS AND TOM WALKED TO
SCHOOL TOGETHER.
WHEN THEY CAME TO THE WIDE
RIVER, THEY LOOKED FOR MONTY.

by James Stevenson

MONTY WAS ALWAYS
ASLEEP, SNORING.

WAKE UP, MONTY!
THIS IS A SCHOOL DAY!

THEY CLIMBED ON
MONTY'S BACK, AND
HE SWAM ACROSS
THE RIVER.

WHEN THEY GOT TO THE FAR SIDE,
DORIS AND ARTHUR AND TOM WENT
TO SCHOOL. MONTY WENT BACK
TO SLEEP.

...GUG..GUGGLE...

EVERY AFTERNOON, HE
GAVE THEM A RIDE BACK.

DON'T GET
OUR BOOKS
WET !

MORE TO
THE RIGHT !

HURRY UP !
WE WANT TO
GET HOME !

...BUT MONTY
DID NOT COME.

THEN MONTY FLOATED BY.

MONTY! WHERE HAVE YOU BEEN?

I AM ON VACATION.

THIS IS NOT VACATION TIME!

IT IS FOR ME. THIS IS ALLIGATOR VACATION.

11

WELL, WHAT ARE WE SUPPOSED TO DO NOW?

IT BEATS ME.

EVERYBODY START THINKING.

WHAT ARE YOU THINKING, DORIS?

I'M THINKING WE NEED A NEW ALLIGATOR.

THAT'S NOT THINKING. THAT'S JUST WISHING.

PARDON US FOR LIVING...   WHO WANTS TO WATCH A DUCK THINK, ANYWAY?

THAT'S ALL I NEED...FOUR TURTLES...

..ALL I NEED?.....

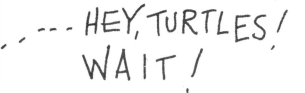

--- HEY, TURTLES! WAIT!

17

THEY WENT BACK TO SHORE, AND PUT THEIR BOOKS IN THE SUN TO DRY. TOM AND DORIS SAT DOWN.

HEY... I FOUND A BOARD!

HERE'S MY PLAN: YOU SIT ON
THE BOARD, TOM.. AND I'LL JUMP
OUT OF THE TREE ONTO THE
OTHER END OF THE BOARD,
AND YOU'LL GO FLYING
RIGHT ACROSS THE
RIVER!

THEY DECIDED TO TRY IT WITH DORIS BECAUSE SHE WAS THE LIGHTEST. DORIS STOOD ON THE BOARD.

READY, DORIS?

I SUPPOSE SO.

IT WAS CLEAR THAT THEY WOULD HAVE TO SWIM ACROSS.

HANG ON, TOM..

KEEP THE BOOKS DRY

STEADY.. HERE WE GO..

MORE TO THE RIGHT, ARTHUR

SLOW DOWN

GO FASTER

STRAIGHT AHEAD, ARTHUR

DON'T WOBBLE, ARTHUR

SIT STILL, TOM

BE QUIET

STOP TELLING ME WHAT TO DO!

STOP TELLING ME WHAT TO DO!

STOP TELLING ME WHAT TO DO!

WE THOUGHT YOU WERE ON VACATION...
I AM, BUT SOMETIMES WHEN I AM ON VACATION I TAKE A DAY OFF

THANKS FOR THE RIDE, MONTY!

IS THERE ANY CHANCE YOU'LL BE HERE THIS AFTERNOON, MONTY?

MONTY?

GUG... GUGGLE..

BUT MONTY HAD ALREADY STARTED TO SNORE.

The truth about alligators

> Did you know that crocodiles and alligators both belong to a group of reptiles called crocodilians? Crocodilians are the largest reptiles and live mostly in fresh water – rivers, swamps and lakes.

There are three different groups of crocodilians:

alligator   crocodile   gavial

> All three groups of crocodilians look very much alike. So then, how can you tell them apart? Each kind of crocodilian has a different shaped jaw or snout.

Alligators have broad, round snouts. When their mouths are closed, the fourth tooth in the lower jaw does not show, but fits into a groove in the upper jaw.

Crocodiles have long, pointed snouts. When their mouths are closed, the fourth tooth in the lower jaw pokes out.

Gavials have long, thin snouts, like beaks. The front teeth are larger than the back teeth.

Did you know that...?

Alligators hide beneath the water waiting for their victims. They can do this because their eyes and ears are placed on top of their heads.

Alligators are found in Central and South America and can grow to a length of 5.8 metres.

Alligators are survivors from a group of reptiles to which the dinosaur and pterodactyl also belonged.

The name *alligator* comes from a Spanish word meaning *lizard*. It was given by Spanish settlers who landed in these parts of America.

Alligators eat birds, snakes, turtles and frogs. They swallow their food whole.

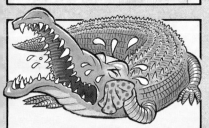

Alligators and crocodiles don't cry tears! As their jaws stretch to swallow a chunk of meat, their eyes water so that it looks as if they are crying.

An alligator's large throat helps it to swallow larger animals. It kills them by holding them under water until they drown.

The mother alligator produces eggs. Here, the baby alligators are hatching out.

SCHOOLS YESTERDAY

Just over a hundred years ago a new law was passed. For the first time in history all children in Britain would have to go to school.

As there weren't enough schools, lots of new ones had to be built. One of the first to open was this London school.

All the infant classrooms were on the ground floor. The older girls were on the first floor and the older boys were right at the top of the building. Girls and boys went into school through different doors.

Look at the tall, narrow windows. Sometimes they had coloured glass in them like a church. It stopped the children from looking outside.

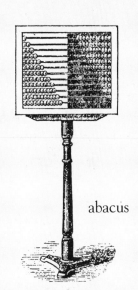

abacus

Schools had chimneys too, to let out the smoke from the coal fires.

All the lavatories were outside in the school yard.

Inside, several children had to sit at one long desk. There were no backrests but they still had to sit up very straight.

They learnt to count with an abacus on a stand and learnt to sing when the teacher played the harmonium.

Rough Inventory of Furniture.

School Room:
  10 desks   12.0 long   convertible
  4   "   6.0   "   "
  1 master's desk; 1 table; 1 bench; 1 harmonium;
  1 blackboard on stand; 2 blackboards (ordinary);
  1 easel; 1 cupboard 2.6 x 2.6 x 1.6; 1 clock; 1 press;
  1 fender; 1 T-square; maps; pictures, etc.

Class Rooms:
  8 Desks   6.0 long   convertible
  1 chair; 1 blackboard on stand; 1 clock; 1 lamp;
  1 coal scuttle; 1 fire-guard; maps, etc.

Infant School:
  4 Desks   6.0 long convertible with backs new
  4   "   6.0   "   "   "   "   old
  4 benches with backs; 2 chairs; 1 cupboard 6.0 x 6.0 x 1.6
  2 blackboards; 1 easel; 1 press; 1 globe; 1 fender;
  lamps; pictures, etc.

Note: measurements given are in feet and inches.
1 foot = 30.5 centimetres.

desks

37

Every day the teacher had to write in the log book or school diary. Sometimes it was about the weather, sometimes about the lessons, sometimes about the children and sometimes about visitors to the school.

Read what the teacher wrote in the log book of Oadby Board School, which opened in 1872.

Monday July 22nd 1872
Opened the school at 9 o'clock and admitted 36 scholars. Admitted 3 more in the afternoon.

Monday September 27th 1872
Sent a boy home this morning to wash his hands and face.

Monday October 14th 1872
Began to have fires today because it was very cold in the morning. Children unable to go in the playground so marched in school instead.

Wednesday July 2nd 1873
Had to use the cane to several of the half-timers this afternoon because they did not mind what was said to them.

Wednesday July 30th 1873
Allowed the children to have a bucket of water and a jug, to drink during playtime.

Wednesday October 1st 1873
Children sang and repeated tables when they came in from the playground this afternoon instead of their ordinary lessons.

Thursday February 27th 1874
Received some pens, ink and blotting paper for the use of the school and gave each child who had a copy-book a new pen and holder.

June 23rd 1877
Taught two of the elder girls how to knit stockings. Punished a boy on Friday for throwing a stone over the wall.

February 4th 1882
Mr. Blakiston visited and examined the school on Wednesday and Thursday. Out of 37 children presented in Standard 1, 29 passed in Reading and writing and 33 in Arithmetic.

It's great fun looking at old school photographs. You can see what the children and the teachers looked like and the clothes they used to wear to school. In some of the photographs you can see inside the classrooms and at what the children did at school. People don't always smile in old photographs, because the camera took a long time to work. The children often felt rather bored.

Class 1V at Whalley National School, Lancashire in 1906.

The sewing class at Cromer Street School, London in 1906.

Lining up to go into Sutton Primary School in Hull.

40

Five to a desk at Laygate School, South Shields.

Exercising with dumb-bells in Leeds in 1900.

Bramshaw County Primary School in 1898 and below in 1969.

Some schools have their own collection of photographs. Taking a look at these shows up the things that have changed. Children seem much the same.

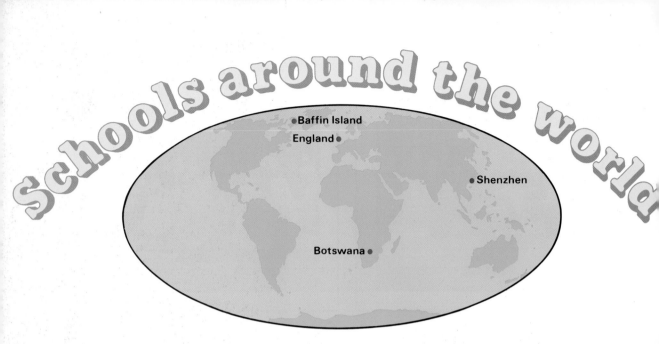

Baffin Island

England

Shenzhen

Botswana

Children all over the world go to school. They all learn to read and write and study maths. Yet, in some ways, schools can be very different.

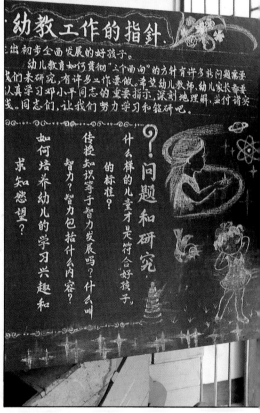

This is a school in Shenzhen in China. The children's first language is Chinese.

This beautifully written message tells the parents "how to develop good, balanced children".

42

This Innuit boy lives on Baffin Island in Canada. He and his friends travel a long way to school. They take sandwiches for lunch. Seals and polar bears live on Baffin Island, and fish, dolphins and whales swim in the sea.

At this school in Botswana in Africa, so many children wanted to come to school that this class had to be held outside. How often could you have lessons outside where you live?

This school in England travels to a new town each week. It is part of Robert Brothers' Famous Circus. The children share their lives with elephants and camels and their parents are clowns, acrobats and trapeze artistes.

Today Was a Terrible Day.

Today was a terrible day. It started when I dropped my pencil. Miss Tyler asked, "Ronald Morgan, why are you crawling under the table like a snake?"

Now all the children call me Snakey.

When Miss Tyler told us to take out last night's homework, I noticed that my mother had forgotten to sign mine. I quickly signed it for her so she wouldn't get into trouble.

But Miss Tyler said, "Ronald Morgan. It is a crime to sign other people's names. And you spelt your mother's name wrongly." All the children laughed.

Later, when Billy was reading — he's in the Satellite group — I got hungry, and my stomach made noises. I tiptoed to the cupboard and ate a ham sandwich. But I had the wrong bag. It was Jimmy's lunch.

"Ronald Morgan, is that you chewing?" Miss Tyler asked. All the children looked at me. And Jimmy cried because he didn't want my sandwich.

Then, when Alice was reading — she's in the Mariners — my group had to do a workbook page. I didn't remember how to do it so I asked Rosemary.

"Don't you even know how to do that?" Rosemary asked. And she's in the lower group, just like me.

After I had finished the workbook page, I wrote my initials on the thirsty sheet and went into the hall for a drink of water. Mrs. Gallop's class was having free time, and I stood in line with them.

"Hi, Johnny," I said, and he said hi to me. He showed me how to hold my finger over the tap. Some of the water landed on the floor. Most of it landed on Joy Farley's dress.

Mrs. Gallop took me to Miss Tyler and said, "Ronald Morgan may never get to my class if he doesn't learn to behave himself."

And I heard Rosemary say, "Ronald Morgan may never get to her class anyway. He still can't read."

During our free time we went outside
to play ball. I played fielder because
I don't catch very well. Only one ball
came near me. I ran for it. I missed it,
and my ice-cream money fell out of my
pocket.

   "You've just lost the game, Snakey,"
Billy yelled. And Tom said, "What did
you expect from that kid?"

When lunchtime came, I had no money for ice-cream. I watched Jimmy eat my peanut-butter sandwich. He said he'd starve to death without it.

So all I had was half of Rosemary's chocolate bar and one of Billy's biscuits.

fter lunch Miss Tyler called the Rockets to the reading circle. I'm a Rocket. Rosemary read the first sentence. And Tom read the next one. They didn't make any mistakes today.

When it was my turn, I said, "Sally was a horse."

Miss Tyler said, "Ronald Morgan. That's not right."

Rosemary said, "Sally *saw* a *house*." And Tom said, "Some Rocket you are."

It was almost time to go home. Miss Tyler said, "I think the plant monitor has forgotten to water the plants again."

Guess who the plant monitor is? I got up and watered all the plants, but while I was doing the last one, the best one, I looked out of the window. Somehow I knocked the pot off the windowsill.

When it was finally time to go home, Miss Tyler gave me a note. "Ronald Morgan," she said. "Take this note home. Try to read it by yourself. If you can't I'm sure your mother will help you."

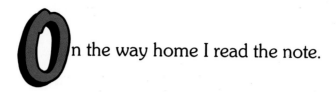

On the way home I read the note.

Dear Ronald,
    I'm sorry you had a sad day.
    Tomorrow will be a happy day because it's my birthday.
    You and I will make it happy.
                Love,
                Miss Tyler

Hey.
I read that whole note by myself.
I can read.

Wait until I tell Michael. He's my best friend.

Hello, Michael? This is Snakey. Guess what? I've just found out I can read. And guess what *else*? It's Miss Tyler's birthday.

I think I'll take her a plant. I know she needs one."

by Patricia Reilly Giff,
illustrated by Susanna Natti

Back to School

In the last week of the holidays
I was feeling glum.
I could hardly wait for school to start;
Neither could Mum.

Now we've been back a week,
I could do with a breather.
I can hardly wait for the holidays,
Teacher can't either.

by Allan Ahlberg